www.FlowerpotPress.com
PAB-0808-0270 · 978-1-68461-060-0
Made in China/Fabriqué en Chine

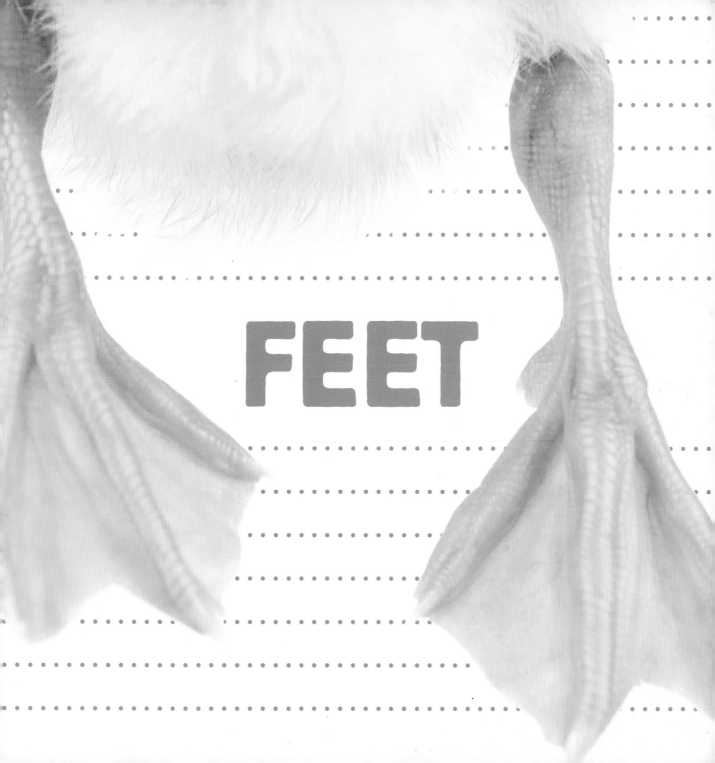

FEET

Who has

HAPPY FEET

like these?

A penguin!

Who has
SCALY FEET
like this?

A crocodile!

Who has HOOFED FEET like these?

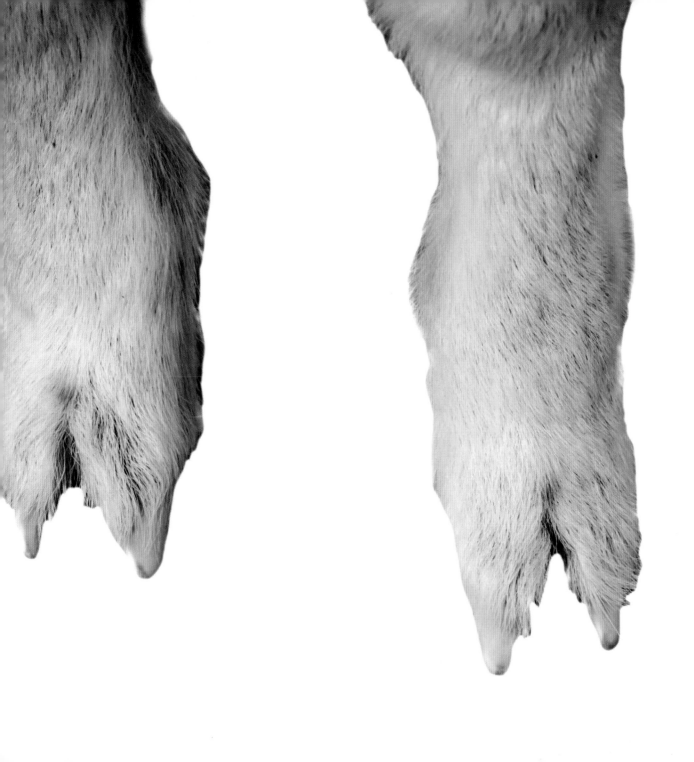

A goat!

Who has WEBBED FEET like these?

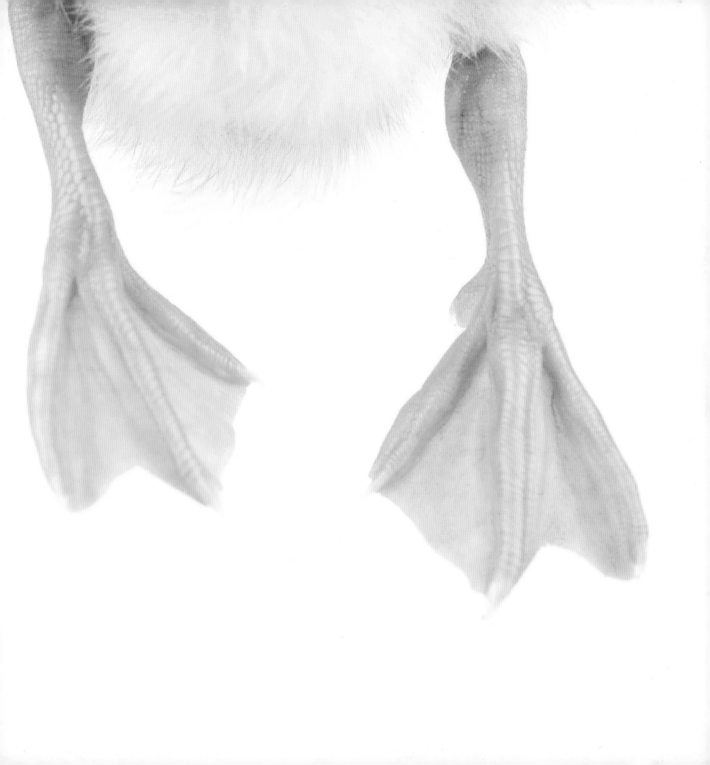

A duck!

Who has SPOTTED FEET like these?

A leopard!

Who has COLD FEET like these?

A polar bear!

Who has
FAST FEET
like these?

An ostrich!